this

Blood Pressure Log Book

BELONGS TO:

....

IN CASE OF EMERGENCY PLEASE CONTACT:

....

....

....

IMPORTANT INFORMATION:
(DOCTOR, MEDICATION / DOSE, BLOOD TYPE)

....

....

....

....

....

....

Week_____

Weight_____

Mood ☺ ☺ ☺ ☺ ☺

Date	Time	Systolic	Diastolic	Heart Rate	Notes
MON __/__/__	am				
	am				
	pm				
	pm				
TUES __/__/__	am				
	am				
	pm				
	pm				
WEDS __/__/__	am				
	am				
	pm				
	pm				
THURS __/__/__	am				
	am				
	pm				
	pm				
FRI __/__/__	am				
	am				
	pm				
	pm				
SAT __/__/__	am				
	am				
	pm				
	pm				
SUN __/__/__	am				
	am				
	pm				
	pm				

Week_____

Weight_____

Mood ☺ ☺ ☺ ☺ ☺

Date	Time	Systolic	Diastolic	Heart Rate	Notes
MON __ / __ / __	am				
	am				
	pm				
	pm				
TUES __ / __ / __	am				
	am				
	pm				
	pm				
WEDS __ / __ / __	am				
	am				
	pm				
	pm				
THURS __ / __ / __	am				
	am				
	pm				
	pm				
FRI __ / __ / __	am				
	am				
	pm				
	pm				
SAT __ / __ / __	am				
	am				
	pm				
	pm				
SUN __ / __ / __	am				
	am				
	pm				
	pm				

Week _____

Weight _____

Mood ☺ ☺ ☺ ☺ ☺

Date	Time	Systolic	Diastolic	Heart Rate	Notes
MON __ / __ / __	am				
	am				
	pm				
	pm				
TUES __ / __ / __	am				
	am				
	pm				
	pm				
WEDS __ / __ / __	am				
	am				
	pm				
	pm				
THURS __ / __ / __	am				
	am				
	pm				
	pm				
FRI __ / __ / __	am				
	am				
	pm				
	pm				
SAT __ / __ / __	am				
	am				
	pm				
	pm				
SUN __ / __ / __	am				
	am				
	pm				
	pm				

Week _____

Weight _____

Mood ☺ ☺ ☺ ☺ ☺

Date	Time	Systolic	Diastolic	Heart Rate	Notes
MON __/__/__	am				
	am				
	pm				
	pm				
TUES __/__/__	am				
	am				
	pm				
	pm				
WEDS __/__/__	am				
	am				
	pm				
	pm				
THURS __/__/__	am				
	am				
	pm				
	pm				
FRI __/__/__	am				
	am				
	pm				
	pm				
SAT __/__/__	am				
	am				
	pm				
	pm				
SUN __/__/__	am				
	am				
	pm				
	pm				

*Week*_____

*Weight*_____

Mood ☺ ☺ ☺ ☺ ☺

Date	Time	Systolic	Diastolic	Heart Rate	Notes
MON __/__/__	am				
	am				
	pm				
	pm				
TUES __/__/__	am				
	am				
	pm				
	pm				
WEDS __/__/__	am				
	am				
	pm				
	pm				
THURS __/__/__	am				
	am				
	pm				
	pm				
FRI __/__/__	am				
	am				
	pm				
	pm				
SAT __/__/__	am				
	am				
	pm				
	pm				
SUN __/__/__	am				
	am				
	pm				
	pm				

Week_____
Weight_____

Mood ☺ ☺ ☺ ☺ ☺

Date	Time	Systolic	Diastolic	Heart Rate	Notes
MON __/__/__	am				
	am				
	pm				
	pm				
TUES __/__/__	am				
	am				
	pm				
	pm				
WEDS __/__/__	am				
	am				
	pm				
	pm				
THURS __/__/__	am				
	am				
	pm				
	pm				
FRI __/__/__	am				
	am				
	pm				
	pm				
SAT __/__/__	am				
	am				
	pm				
	pm				
SUN __/__/__	am				
	am				
	pm				
	pm				

*Week*_____

*Weight*_____

Mood ☺ ☺ ☺ ☺ ☺

Date	Time	Systolic	Diastolic	Heart Rate	Notes
MON __/__/__	am				
	am				
	pm				
	pm				
TUES __/__/__	am				
	am				
	pm				
	pm				
WEDS __/__/__	am				
	am				
	pm				
	pm				
THURS __/__/__	am				
	am				
	pm				
	pm				
FRI __/__/__	am				
	am				
	pm				
	pm				
SAT __/__/__	am				
	am				
	pm				
	pm				
SUN __/__/__	am				
	am				
	pm				
	pm				

Week_____
Weight_____

Mood  ☺ ☺ ☺ ☺ ☺

Date	Time	Systolic	Diastolic	Heart Rate	Notes
MON __/__/__	am				
	am				
	pm				
	pm				
TUES __/__/__	am				
	am				
	pm				
	pm				
WEDS __/__/__	am				
	am				
	pm				
	pm				
THURS __/__/__	am				
	am				
	pm				
	pm				
FRI __/__/__	am				
	am				
	pm				
	pm				
SAT __/__/__	am				
	am				
	pm				
	pm				
SUN __/__/__	am				
	am				
	pm				
	pm				

*Week*_____

*Weight*_____

Mood ☺ ☺ ☺ ☺ ☺

Date	Time	Systolic	Diastolic	Heart Rate	Notes
MON __/__/__	am				
	am				
	pm				
	pm				
TUES __/__/__	am				
	am				
	pm				
	pm				
WEDS __/__/__	am				
	am				
	pm				
	pm				
THURS __/__/__	am				
	am				
	pm				
	pm				
FRI __/__/__	am				
	am				
	pm				
	pm				
SAT __/__/__	am				
	am				
	pm				
	pm				
SUN __/__/__	am				
	am				
	pm				
	pm				

Week_____
Weight_____

Mood ☺ ☺ ☺ ☺ ☺

Date	Time	Systolic	Diastolic	Heart Rate	Notes
MON __ / __ / __	am				
	am				
	pm				
	pm				
TUES __ / __ / __	am				
	am				
	pm				
	pm				
WEDS __ / __ / __	am				
	am				
	pm				
	pm				
THURS __ / __ / __	am				
	am				
	pm				
	pm				
FRI __ / __ / __	am				
	am				
	pm				
	pm				
SAT __ / __ / __	am				
	am				
	pm				
	pm				
SUN __ / __ / __	am				
	am				
	pm				
	pm				

*Week*_____

*Weight*_____

Mood ☺ ☺ ☺ ☺ ☺

Date	Time	Systolic	Diastolic	Heart Rate	Notes
MON __ /__/__	am				
	am				
	pm				
	pm				
TUES __ /__/__	am				
	am				
	pm				
	pm				
WEDS __ /__/__	am				
	am				
	pm				
	pm				
THURS __ /__/__	am				
	am				
	pm				
	pm				
FRI __ /__/__	am				
	am				
	pm				
	pm				
SAT __ /__/__	am				
	am				
	pm				
	pm				
SUN __ /__/__	am				
	am				
	pm				
	pm				

Week_____

Weight_____

Mood ☺ ☺ ☺ ☺ ☺

Date	Time	Systolic	Diastolic	Heart Rate	Notes
MON __ / __ / __	am				
	am				
	pm				
	pm				
TUES __ / __ / __	am				
	am				
	pm				
	pm				
WEDS __ / __ / __	am				
	am				
	pm				
	pm				
THURS __ / __ / __	am				
	am				
	pm				
	pm				
FRI __ / __ / __	am				
	am				
	pm				
	pm				
SAT __ / __ / __	am				
	am				
	pm				
	pm				
SUN __ / __ / __	am				
	am				
	pm				
	pm				

*Week*_____

*Weight*_____

Mood ☺ ☺ ☺ ☺ ☺

Date	Time	Systolic	Diastolic	Heart Rate	Notes
MON __/__/__	am				
	am				
	pm				
	pm				
TUES __/__/__	am				
	am				
	pm				
	pm				
WEDS __/__/__	am				
	am				
	pm				
	pm				
THURS __/__/__	am				
	am				
	pm				
	pm				
FRI __/__/__	am				
	am				
	pm				
	pm				
SAT __/__/__	am				
	am				
	pm				
	pm				
SUN __/__/__	am				
	am				
	pm				
	pm				

Week_____
Weight_____   Mood ☺ ☺ ☺ ☺ ☺

Date	Time	Systolic	Diastolic	Heart Rate	Notes
MON __/__/__	am				
	am				
	pm				
	pm				
TUES __/__/__	am				
	am				
	pm				
	pm				
WEDS __/__/__	am				
	am				
	pm				
	pm				
THURS __/__/__	am				
	am				
	pm				
	pm				
FRI __/__/__	am				
	am				
	pm				
	pm				
SAT __/__/__	am				
	am				
	pm				
	pm				
SUN __/__/__	am				
	am				
	pm				
	pm				

Week _____

Weight _____

Mood ☺ ☺ ☺ ☺ ☺

Date	Time	Systolic	Diastolic	Heart Rate	Notes
MON __/__/__	am				
	am				
	pm				
	pm				
TUES __/__/__	am				
	am				
	pm				
	pm				
WEDS __/__/__	am				
	am				
	pm				
	pm				
THURS __/__/__	am				
	am				
	pm				
	pm				
FRI __/__/__	am				
	am				
	pm				
	pm				
SAT __/__/__	am				
	am				
	pm				
	pm				
SUN __/__/__	am				
	am				
	pm				
	pm				

Week_____
Weight_____   Mood ☺ ☺ ☺ ☺ ☺

Date	Time	Systolic	Diastolic	Heart Rate	Notes
MON __ / __ / __	am				
	am				
	pm				
	pm				
TUES __ / __ / __	am				
	am				
	pm				
	pm				
WEDS __ / __ / __	am				
	am				
	pm				
	pm				
THURS __ / __ / __	am				
	am				
	pm				
	pm				
FRI __ / __ / __	am				
	am				
	pm				
	pm				
SAT __ / __ / __	am				
	am				
	pm				
	pm				
SUN __ / __ / __	am				
	am				
	pm				
	pm				

*Week*_____

*Weight*_____

Mood ☺ ☺ ☺ ☺ ☺

Date	Time	Systolic	Diastolic	Heart Rate	Notes
MON __/__/__	am				
	am				
	pm				
	pm				
TUES __/__/__	am				
	am				
	pm				
	pm				
WEDS __/__/__	am				
	am				
	pm				
	pm				
THURS __/__/__	am				
	am				
	pm				
	pm				
FRI __/__/__	am				
	am				
	pm				
	pm				
SAT __/__/__	am				
	am				
	pm				
	pm				
SUN __/__/__	am				
	am				
	pm				
	pm				

Week_____

Weight_____

Mood ☺ ☺ ☺ ☺ ☺

Date	Time	Systolic	Diastolic	Heart Rate	Notes
MON __ / __ / __	am				
	am				
	pm				
	pm				
TUES __ / __ / __	am				
	am				
	pm				
	pm				
WEDS __ / __ / __	am				
	am				
	pm				
	pm				
THURS __ / __ / __	am				
	am				
	pm				
	pm				
FRI __ / __ / __	am				
	am				
	pm				
	pm				
SAT __ / __ / __	am				
	am				
	pm				
	pm				
SUN __ / __ / __	am				
	am				
	pm				
	pm				

Week_____

Weight_____

Mood ☺ ☺ ☺ ☺ ☺

Date	Time	Systolic	Diastolic	Heart Rate	Notes
MON __/__/__	am				
	am				
	pm				
	pm				
TUES __/__/__	am				
	am				
	pm				
	pm				
WEDS __/__/__	am				
	am				
	pm				
	pm				
THURS __/__/__	am				
	am				
	pm				
	pm				
FRI __/__/__	am				
	am				
	pm				
	pm				
SAT __/__/__	am				
	am				
	pm				
	pm				
SUN __/__/__	am				
	am				
	pm				
	pm				

Week_____

Weight_____

Mood ☺ ☺ ☺ ☺ ☺

Date	Time	Systolic	Diastolic	Heart Rate	Notes
MON __/__/__	am				
	am				
	pm				
	pm				
TUES __/__/__	am				
	am				
	pm				
	pm				
WEDS __/__/__	am				
	am				
	pm				
	pm				
THURS __/__/__	am				
	am				
	pm				
	pm				
FRI __/__/__	am				
	am				
	pm				
	pm				
SAT __/__/__	am				
	am				
	pm				
	pm				
SUN __/__/__	am				
	am				
	pm				
	pm				

Week_____

Weight_____

Mood ☺ ☺ ☺ ☺ ☺

Date	Time	Systolic	Diastolic	Heart Rate	Notes
MON __/__/__	am				
	am				
	pm				
	pm				
TUES __/__/__	am				
	am				
	pm				
	pm				
WEDS __/__/__	am				
	am				
	pm				
	pm				
THURS __/__/__	am				
	am				
	pm				
	pm				
FRI __/__/__	am				
	am				
	pm				
	pm				
SAT __/__/__	am				
	am				
	pm				
	pm				
SUN __/__/__	am				
	am				
	pm				
	pm				

*Week*_____

*Weight*_____

Mood ☺ ☺ ☺ ☺ ☺

Date	Time	Systolic	Diastolic	Heart Rate	Notes
MON __ / __ / __	am				
	am				
	pm				
	pm				
TUES __ / __ / __	am				
	am				
	pm				
	pm				
WEDS __ / __ / __	am				
	am				
	pm				
	pm				
THURS __ / __ / __	am				
	am				
	pm				
	pm				
FRI __ / __ / __	am				
	am				
	pm				
	pm				
SAT __ / __ / __	am				
	am				
	pm				
	pm				
SUN __ / __ / __	am				
	am				
	pm				
	pm				

Week _____   _Mood_ ☺ ☺ ☺ ☺ ☺

Weight _____

Date	Time	Systolic	Diastolic	Heart Rate	Notes
MON __/__/__	am				
	am				
	pm				
	pm				
TUES __/__/__	am				
	am				
	pm				
	pm				
WEDS __/__/__	am				
	am				
	pm				
	pm				
THURS __/__/__	am				
	am				
	pm				
	pm				
FRI __/__/__	am				
	am				
	pm				
	pm				
SAT __/__/__	am				
	am				
	pm				
	pm				
SUN __/__/__	am				
	am				
	pm				
	pm				

Week_____

Weight_____

Mood  ☺ ☺ ☺ ☺ ☺

Date	Time	Systolic	Diastolic	Heart Rate	Notes
MON __/__/__	am				
	am				
	pm				
	pm				
TUES __/__/__	am				
	am				
	pm				
	pm				
WEDS __/__/__	am				
	am				
	pm				
	pm				
THURS __/__/__	am				
	am				
	pm				
	pm				
FRI __/__/__	am				
	am				
	pm				
	pm				
SAT __/__/__	am				
	am				
	pm				
	pm				
SUN __/__/__	am				
	am				
	pm				
	pm				

Week_____

Weight_____

Mood ☺ ☺ ☺ ☺ ☺

Date	Time	Systolic	Diastolic	Heart Rate	Notes
MON __ / __ / __	am				
	am				
	pm				
	pm				
TUES __ / __ / __	am				
	am				
	pm				
	pm				
WEDS __ / __ / __	am				
	am				
	pm				
	pm				
THURS __ / __ / __	am				
	am				
	pm				
	pm				
FRI __ / __ / __	am				
	am				
	pm				
	pm				
SAT __ / __ / __	am				
	am				
	pm				
	pm				
SUN __ / __ / __	am				
	am				
	pm				
	pm				

Week_____

Weight_____

Mood ☺ ☺ ☺ ☺ ☺

Date	Time	Systolic	Diastolic	Heart Rate	Notes
MON __ / __ / __	am				
	am				
	pm				
	pm				
TUES __ / __ / __	am				
	am				
	pm				
	pm				
WEDS __ / __ / __	am				
	am				
	pm				
	pm				
THURS __ / __ / __	am				
	am				
	pm				
	pm				
FRI __ / __ / __	am				
	am				
	pm				
	pm				
SAT __ / __ / __	am				
	am				
	pm				
	pm				
SUN __ / __ / __	am				
	am				
	pm				
	pm				

_Week_____

_Weight_____

Mood ☺ ☺ ☺ ☺ ☺

Date	Time	Systolic	Diastolic	Heart Rate	Notes
MON __ / __ / __	am				
	am				
	pm				
	pm				
TUES __ / __ / __	am				
	am				
	pm				
	pm				
WEDS __ / __ / __	am				
	am				
	pm				
	pm				
THURS __ / __ / __	am				
	am				
	pm				
	pm				
FRI __ / __ / __	am				
	am				
	pm				
	pm				
SAT __ / __ / __	am				
	am				
	pm				
	pm				
SUN __ / __ / __	am				
	am				
	pm				
	pm				

Week_____

Weight_____

Mood ☺ ☺ ☺ ☺ ☺

Date	Time	Systolic	Diastolic	Heart Rate	Notes
MON __ / __ / __	am				
	am				
	pm				
	pm				
TUES __ / __ / __	am				
	am				
	pm				
	pm				
WEDS __ / __ / __	am				
	am				
	pm				
	pm				
THURS __ / __ / __	am				
	am				
	pm				
	pm				
FRI __ / __ / __	am				
	am				
	pm				
	pm				
SAT __ / __ / __	am				
	am				
	pm				
	pm				
SUN __ / __ / __	am				
	am				
	pm				
	pm				

Week _____

Weight _____

Mood ☺ ☺ ☺ ☺ ☺

Date	Time	Systolic	Diastolic	Heart Rate	Notes
MON __/__/__	am				
	am				
	pm				
	pm				
TUES __/__/__	am				
	am				
	pm				
	pm				
WEDS __/__/__	am				
	am				
	pm				
	pm				
THURS __/__/__	am				
	am				
	pm				
	pm				
FRI __/__/__	am				
	am				
	pm				
	pm				
SAT __/__/__	am				
	am				
	pm				
	pm				
SUN __/__/__	am				
	am				
	pm				
	pm				

Week _____

Weight _____

Mood ☺ ☺ ☺ ☺ ☺

Date	Time	Systolic	Diastolic	Heart Rate	Notes
MON __/__/__	am				
	am				
	pm				
	pm				
TUES __/__/__	am				
	am				
	pm				
	pm				
WEDS __/__/__	am				
	am				
	pm				
	pm				
THURS __/__/__	am				
	am				
	pm				
	pm				
FRI __/__/__	am				
	am				
	pm				
	pm				
SAT __/__/__	am				
	am				
	pm				
	pm				
SUN __/__/__	am				
	am				
	pm				
	pm				

*Week*_____

*Weight*_____

Mood ☺ ☺ ☺ ☺ ☺

Date	Time	Systolic	Diastolic	Heart Rate	Notes
MON __ / __ / __	am				
	am				
	pm				
	pm				
TUES __ / __ / __	am				
	am				
	pm				
	pm				
WEDS __ / __ / __	am				
	am				
	pm				
	pm				
THURS __ / __ / __	am				
	am				
	pm				
	pm				
FRI __ / __ / __	am				
	am				
	pm				
	pm				
SAT __ / __ / __	am				
	am				
	pm				
	pm				
SUN __ / __ / __	am				
	am				
	pm				
	pm				

Week_____

Weight_____

Mood ☺ ☺ ☺ ☺ ☺

Date	Time	Systolic	Diastolic	Heart Rate	Notes
MON __ / __ / __	am				
	am				
	pm				
	pm				
TUES __ / __ / __	am				
	am				
	pm				
	pm				
WEDS __ / __ / __	am				
	am				
	pm				
	pm				
THURS __ / __ / __	am				
	am				
	pm				
	pm				
FRI __ / __ / __	am				
	am				
	pm				
	pm				
SAT __ / __ / __	am				
	am				
	pm				
	pm				
SUN __ / __ / __	am				
	am				
	pm				
	pm				

Week _____

Weight _____

Mood ☺ ☺ ☺ ☺ ☺

Date	Time	Systolic	Diastolic	Heart Rate	Notes
MON __ / __ / __	am				
	am				
	pm				
	pm				
TUES __ / __ / __	am				
	am				
	pm				
	pm				
WEDS __ / __ / __	am				
	am				
	pm				
	pm				
THURS __ / __ / __	am				
	am				
	pm				
	pm				
FRI __ / __ / __	am				
	am				
	pm				
	pm				
SAT __ / __ / __	am				
	am				
	pm				
	pm				
SUN __ / __ / __	am				
	am				
	pm				
	pm				

Week _____

Weight _____

Mood ☺ ☺ ☺ ☺ ☺

Date	Time	Systolic	Diastolic	Heart Rate	Notes
MON __ / __ / __	am				
	am				
	pm				
	pm				
TUES __ / __ / __	am				
	am				
	pm				
	pm				
WEDS __ / __ / __	am				
	am				
	pm				
	pm				
THURS __ / __ / __	am				
	am				
	pm				
	pm				
FRI __ / __ / __	am				
	am				
	pm				
	pm				
SAT __ / __ / __	am				
	am				
	pm				
	pm				
SUN __ / __ / __	am				
	am				
	pm				
	pm				

*Week*_____

*Weight*_____

Mood ☺ ☺ ☺ ☺ ☺

Date	Time	Systolic	Diastolic	Heart Rate	Notes
MON __ / __ / __	am				
	am				
	pm				
	pm				
TUES __ / __ / __	am				
	am				
	pm				
	pm				
WEDS __ / __ / __	am				
	am				
	pm				
	pm				
THURS __ / __ / __	am				
	am				
	pm				
	pm				
FRI __ / __ / __	am				
	am				
	pm				
	pm				
SAT __ / __ / __	am				
	am				
	pm				
	pm				
SUN __ / __ / __	am				
	am				
	pm				
	pm				

Week _____

Weight _____

Mood ☺ ☺ ☺ ☺ ☺

Date	Time	Systolic	Diastolic	Heart Rate	Notes
MON __ / __ / __	am				
	am				
	pm				
	pm				
TUES __ / __ / __	am				
	am				
	pm				
	pm				
WEDS __ / __ / __	am				
	am				
	pm				
	pm				
THURS __ / __ / __	am				
	am				
	pm				
	pm				
FRI __ / __ / __	am				
	am				
	pm				
	pm				
SAT __ / __ / __	am				
	am				
	pm				
	pm				
SUN __ / __ / __	am				
	am				
	pm				
	pm				

Week_____

Weight_____

Mood ☺ ☺ ☺ ☺ ☺

Date	Time	Systolic	Diastolic	Heart Rate	Notes
MON __ / __ / __	am				
	am				
	pm				
	pm				
TUES __ / __ / __	am				
	am				
	pm				
	pm				
WEDS __ / __ / __	am				
	am				
	pm				
	pm				
THURS __ / __ / __	am				
	am				
	pm				
	pm				
FRI __ / __ / __	am				
	am				
	pm				
	pm				
SAT __ / __ / __	am				
	am				
	pm				
	pm				
SUN __ / __ / __	am				
	am				
	pm				
	pm				

Week_____

Weight_____

Mood 😊 😊 😊 😊 😊

Date	Time	Systolic	Diastolic	Heart Rate	Notes
MON __/__/__	am				
	am				
	pm				
	pm				
TUES __/__/__	am				
	am				
	pm				
	pm				
WEDS __/__/__	am				
	am				
	pm				
	pm				
THURS __/__/__	am				
	am				
	pm				
	pm				
FRI __/__/__	am				
	am				
	pm				
	pm				
SAT __/__/__	am				
	am				
	pm				
	pm				
SUN __/__/__	am				
	am				
	pm				
	pm				

*Week*_____

*Weight*_____

Mood ☺ ☺ ☺ ☺ ☺

Date	Time	Systolic	Diastolic	Heart Rate	Notes
MON __ / __ / __	am				
	am				
	pm				
	pm				
TUES __ / __ / __	am				
	am				
	pm				
	pm				
WEDS __ / __ / __	am				
	am				
	pm				
	pm				
THURS __ / __ / __	am				
	am				
	pm				
	pm				
FRI __ / __ / __	am				
	am				
	pm				
	pm				
SAT __ / __ / __	am				
	am				
	pm				
	pm				
SUN __ / __ / __	am				
	am				
	pm				
	pm				

Week_____
Weight_____

Mood ☺ ☺ ☺ ☺ ☺

Date	Time	Systolic	Diastolic	Heart Rate	Notes
MON __/__/__	am				
	am				
	pm				
	pm				
TUES __/__/__	am				
	am				
	pm				
	pm				
WEDS __/__/__	am				
	am				
	pm				
	pm				
THURS __/__/__	am				
	am				
	pm				
	pm				
FRI __/__/__	am				
	am				
	pm				
	pm				
SAT __/__/__	am				
	am				
	pm				
	pm				
SUN __/__/__	am				
	am				
	pm				
	pm				

*Week*_____

*Weight*_____

Mood ☺ ☺ ☺ ☺ ☺

Date	Time	Systolic	Diastolic	Heart Rate	Notes
MON __/__/__	am				
	am				
	pm				
	pm				
TUES __/__/__	am				
	am				
	pm				
	pm				
WEDS __/__/__	am				
	am				
	pm				
	pm				
THURS __/__/__	am				
	am				
	pm				
	pm				
FRI __/__/__	am				
	am				
	pm				
	pm				
SAT __/__/__	am				
	am				
	pm				
	pm				
SUN __/__/__	am				
	am				
	pm				
	pm				

Week_____

Weight_____   Mood ☺ ☺ ☺ ☺ ☺

Date	Time	Systolic	Diastolic	Heart Rate	Notes
MON __/__/__	am				
	am				
	pm				
	pm				
TUES __/__/__	am				
	am				
	pm				
	pm				
WEDS __/__/__	am				
	am				
	pm				
	pm				
THURS __/__/__	am				
	am				
	pm				
	pm				
FRI __/__/__	am				
	am				
	pm				
	pm				
SAT __/__/__	am				
	am				
	pm				
	pm				
SUN __/__/__	am				
	am				
	pm				
	pm				

*Week*_____

*Weight*_____

Mood ☺ ☺ ☺ ☺ ☺

Date	Time	Systolic	Diastolic	Heart Rate	Notes
MON __ / __ / __	am				
	am				
	pm				
	pm				
TUES __ / __ / __	am				
	am				
	pm				
	pm				
WEDS __ / __ / __	am				
	am				
	pm				
	pm				
THURS __ / __ / __	am				
	am				
	pm				
	pm				
FRI __ / __ / __	am				
	am				
	pm				
	pm				
SAT __ / __ / __	am				
	am				
	pm				
	pm				
SUN __ / __ / __	am				
	am				
	pm				
	pm				

Week_____
Weight_____   Mood ☺ ☺ ☺ ☺ ☺

Date	Time	Systolic	Diastolic	Heart Rate	Notes
MON __/__/__	am				
	am				
	pm				
	pm				
TUES __/__/__	am				
	am				
	pm				
	pm				
WEDS __/__/__	am				
	am				
	pm				
	pm				
THURS __/__/__	am				
	am				
	pm				
	pm				
FRI __/__/__	am				
	am				
	pm				
	pm				
SAT __/__/__	am				
	am				
	pm				
	pm				
SUN __/__/__	am				
	am				
	pm				
	pm				

Week_____
Weight_____

Mood ☺ ☺ ☺ ☺ ☺

Date	Time	Systolic	Diastolic	Heart Rate	Notes
MON __/__/__	am				
	am				
	pm				
	pm				
TUES __/__/__	am				
	am				
	pm				
	pm				
WEDS __/__/__	am				
	am				
	pm				
	pm				
THURS __/__/__	am				
	am				
	pm				
	pm				
FRI __/__/__	am				
	am				
	pm				
	pm				
SAT __/__/__	am				
	am				
	pm				
	pm				
SUN __/__/__	am				
	am				
	pm				
	pm				

Week_____

Weight_____

Mood ☺ ☺ ☺ ☺ ☺

Date	Time	Systolic	Diastolic	Heart Rate	Notes
MON __ / __ / __	am				
	am				
	pm				
	pm				
TUES __ / __ / __	am				
	am				
	pm				
	pm				
WEDS __ / __ / __	am				
	am				
	pm				
	pm				
THURS __ / __ / __	am				
	am				
	pm				
	pm				
FRI __ / __ / __	am				
	am				
	pm				
	pm				
SAT __ / __ / __	am				
	am				
	pm				
	pm				
SUN __ / __ / __	am				
	am				
	pm				
	pm				

Week _____

Weight _____

Mood ☺ ☺ ☺ ☺ ☺

Date	Time	Systolic	Diastolic	Heart Rate	Notes
MON __ / __ / __	am				
	am				
	pm				
	pm				
TUES __ / __ / __	am				
	am				
	pm				
	pm				
WEDS __ / __ / __	am				
	am				
	pm				
	pm				
THURS __ / __ / __	am				
	am				
	pm				
	pm				
FRI __ / __ / __	am				
	am				
	pm				
	pm				
SAT __ / __ / __	am				
	am				
	pm				
	pm				
SUN __ / __ / __	am				
	am				
	pm				
	pm				

Week_____
Weight_____

Mood ☺ ☺ ☺ ☺ ☺

Date	Time	Systolic	Diastolic	Heart Rate	Notes
MON __ / __ / __	am				
	am				
	pm				
	pm				
TUES __ / __ / __	am				
	am				
	pm				
	pm				
WEDS __ / __ / __	am				
	am				
	pm				
	pm				
THURS __ / __ / __	am				
	am				
	pm				
	pm				
FRI __ / __ / __	am				
	am				
	pm				
	pm				
SAT __ / __ / __	am				
	am				
	pm				
	pm				
SUN __ / __ / __	am				
	am				
	pm				
	pm				

Week _____

Weight _____

Mood ☺ ☺ ☺ ☺ ☺

Date	Time	Systolic	Diastolic	Heart Rate	Notes
MON __ / __ / __	am				
	am				
	pm				
	pm				
TUES __ / __ / __	am				
	am				
	pm				
	pm				
WEDS __ / __ / __	am				
	am				
	pm				
	pm				
THURS __ / __ / __	am				
	am				
	pm				
	pm				
FRI __ / __ / __	am				
	am				
	pm				
	pm				
SAT __ / __ / __	am				
	am				
	pm				
	pm				
SUN __ / __ / __	am				
	am				
	pm				
	pm				

*Week*_____

*Weight*_____

Mood ☺ ☺ ☺ ☺ ☺

Date	Time	Systolic	Diastolic	Heart Rate	Notes
MON __/__/__	am				
	am				
	pm				
	pm				
TUES __/__/__	am				
	am				
	pm				
	pm				
WEDS __/__/__	am				
	am				
	pm				
	pm				
THURS __/__/__	am				
	am				
	pm				
	pm				
FRI __/__/__	am				
	am				
	pm				
	pm				
SAT __/__/__	am				
	am				
	pm				
	pm				
SUN __/__/__	am				
	am				
	pm				
	pm				

Week_____

Weight_____

Mood ☺ ☺ ☺ ☺ ☺

Date	Time	Systolic	Diastolic	Heart Rate	Notes
MON __ / __ / __	am				
	am				
	pm				
	pm				
TUES __ / __ / __	am				
	am				
	pm				
	pm				
WEDS __ / __ / __	am				
	am				
	pm				
	pm				
THURS __ / __ / __	am				
	am				
	pm				
	pm				
FRI __ / __ / __	am				
	am				
	pm				
	pm				
SAT __ / __ / __	am				
	am				
	pm				
	pm				
SUN __ / __ / __	am				
	am				
	pm				
	pm				

Week_____

Weight_____

Mood ☺ ☺ ☺ ☺ ☺

Date	Time	Systolic	Diastolic	Heart Rate	Notes
MON __/__/__	am				
	am				
	pm				
	pm				
TUES __/__/__	am				
	am				
	pm				
	pm				
WEDS __/__/__	am				
	am				
	pm				
	pm				
THURS __/__/__	am				
	am				
	pm				
	pm				
FRI __/__/__	am				
	am				
	pm				
	pm				
SAT __/__/__	am				
	am				
	pm				
	pm				
SUN __/__/__	am				
	am				
	pm				
	pm				

Week_____

Weight_____

Mood ☺ ☺ ☺ ☺ ☺

Date	Time	Systolic	Diastolic	Heart Rate	Notes
MON __ /__ /__	am				
	am				
	pm				
	pm				
TUES __ /__ /__	am				
	am				
	pm				
	pm				
WEDS __ /__ /__	am				
	am				
	pm				
	pm				
THURS __ /__ /__	am				
	am				
	pm				
	pm				
FRI __ /__ /__	am				
	am				
	pm				
	pm				
SAT __ /__ /__	am				
	am				
	pm				
	pm				
SUN __ /__ /__	am				
	am				
	pm				
	pm				

Week_____
Weight_____   Mood ☺ ☺ ☺ ☺ ☺

Date	Time	Systolic	Diastolic	Heart Rate	Notes
MON __/__/__	am				
	am				
	pm				
	pm				
TUES __/__/__	am				
	am				
	pm				
	pm				
WEDS __/__/__	am				
	am				
	pm				
	pm				
THURS __/__/__	am				
	am				
	pm				
	pm				
FRI __/__/__	am				
	am				
	pm				
	pm				
SAT __/__/__	am				
	am				
	pm				
	pm				
SUN __/__/__	am				
	am				
	pm				
	pm				

Week _____

Weight _____

Mood ☺ ☺ ☺ ☺ ☺

Date	Time	Systolic	Diastolic	Heart Rate	Notes
MON __ / __ / __	am				
	am				
	pm				
	pm				
TUES __ / __ / __	am				
	am				
	pm				
	pm				
WEDS __ / __ / __	am				
	am				
	pm				
	pm				
THURS __ / __ / __	am				
	am				
	pm				
	pm				
FRI __ / __ / __	am				
	am				
	pm				
	pm				
SAT __ / __ / __	am				
	am				
	pm				
	pm				
SUN __ / __ / __	am				
	am				
	pm				
	pm				

Week_____

Weight_____

Mood ☺ ☺ ☺ ☺ ☺

Date	Time	Systolic	Diastolic	Heart Rate	Notes
MON __ / __ / __	am				
	am				
	pm				
	pm				
TUES __ / __ / __	am				
	am				
	pm				
	pm				
WEDS __ / __ / __	am				
	am				
	pm				
	pm				
THURS __ / __ / __	am				
	am				
	pm				
	pm				
FRI __ / __ / __	am				
	am				
	pm				
	pm				
SAT __ / __ / __	am				
	am				
	pm				
	pm				
SUN __ / __ / __	am				
	am				
	pm				
	pm				

Week_____
Weight_____

Mood ☺ ☺ ☺ ☺ ☺

Date	Time	Systolic	Diastolic	Heart Rate	Notes
MON __/__/__	am				
	am				
	pm				
	pm				
TUES __/__/__	am				
	am				
	pm				
	pm				
WEDS __/__/__	am				
	am				
	pm				
	pm				
THURS __/__/__	am				
	am				
	pm				
	pm				
FRI __/__/__	am				
	am				
	pm				
	pm				
SAT __/__/__	am				
	am				
	pm				
	pm				
SUN __/__/__	am				
	am				
	pm				
	pm				

Week _____

Weight _____

Mood

Date	Time	Systolic	Diastolic	Heart Rate	Notes
MON __/__/__	am				
	am				
	pm				
	pm				
TUES __/__/__	am				
	am				
	pm				
	pm				
WEDS __/__/__	am				
	am				
	pm				
	pm				
THURS __/__/__	am				
	am				
	pm				
	pm				
FRI __/__/__	am				
	am				
	pm				
	pm				
SAT __/__/__	am				
	am				
	pm				
	pm				
SUN __/__/__	am				
	am				
	pm				
	pm				

*Week*_____

*Weight*_____

Mood ☺ ☺ ☺ ☺ ☺

Date	Time	Systolic	Diastolic	Heart Rate	Notes
MON __/__/__	am				
	am				
	pm				
	pm				
TUES __/__/__	am				
	am				
	pm				
	pm				
WEDS __/__/__	am				
	am				
	pm				
	pm				
THURS __/__/__	am				
	am				
	pm				
	pm				
FRI __/__/__	am				
	am				
	pm				
	pm				
SAT __/__/__	am				
	am				
	pm				
	pm				
SUN __/__/__	am				
	am				
	pm				
	pm				

*Week*_____

*Weight*_____   *Mood* ☺ ☺ ☺ ☺ ☺

Date	Time	Systolic	Diastolic	Heart Rate	Notes
MON __/__/__	am				
	am				
	pm				
	pm				
TUES __/__/__	am				
	am				
	pm				
	pm				
WEDS __/__/__	am				
	am				
	pm				
	pm				
THURS __/__/__	am				
	am				
	pm				
	pm				
FRI __/__/__	am				
	am				
	pm				
	pm				
SAT __/__/__	am				
	am				
	pm				
	pm				
SUN __/__/__	am				
	am				
	pm				
	pm				

Week _____

Weight _____

Mood ☺ ☺ ☺ ☺ ☺

Date	Time	Systolic	Diastolic	Heart Rate	Notes
MON __ / __ / __	am				
	am				
	pm				
	pm				
TUES __ / __ / __	am				
	am				
	pm				
	pm				
WEDS __ / __ / __	am				
	am				
	pm				
	pm				
THURS __ / __ / __	am				
	am				
	pm				
	pm				
FRI __ / __ / __	am				
	am				
	pm				
	pm				
SAT __ / __ / __	am				
	am				
	pm				
	pm				
SUN __ / __ / __	am				
	am				
	pm				
	pm				

_Week_____

_Weight_____

Mood  ☺ ☺ ☺ ☺ ☺

Date	Time	Systolic	Diastolic	Heart Rate	Notes
MON __/__/__	am				
	am				
	pm				
	pm				
TUES __/__/__	am				
	am				
	pm				
	pm				
WEDS __/__/__	am				
	am				
	pm				
	pm				
THURS __/__/__	am				
	am				
	pm				
	pm				
FRI __/__/__	am				
	am				
	pm				
	pm				
SAT __/__/__	am				
	am				
	pm				
	pm				
SUN __/__/__	am				
	am				
	pm				
	pm				

Week _____

Weight _____

Mood ☺ ☺ ☺ ☺ ☺

Date	Time	Systolic	Diastolic	Heart Rate	Notes
MON __ / __ / __	am				
	am				
	pm				
	pm				
TUES __ / __ / __	am				
	am				
	pm				
	pm				
WEDS __ / __ / __	am				
	am				
	pm				
	pm				
THURS __ / __ / __	am				
	am				
	pm				
	pm				
FRI __ / __ / __	am				
	am				
	pm				
	pm				
SAT __ / __ / __	am				
	am				
	pm				
	pm				
SUN __ / __ / __	am				
	am				
	pm				
	pm				

_Week_____

_Weight_____

Mood ☺ ☺ ☺ ☺ ☺

Date	Time	Systolic	Diastolic	Heart Rate	Notes
MON __ / __ / __	am				
	am				
	pm				
	pm				
TUES __ / __ / __	am				
	am				
	pm				
	pm				
WEDS __ / __ / __	am				
	am				
	pm				
	pm				
THURS __ / __ / __	am				
	am				
	pm				
	pm				
FRI __ / __ / __	am				
	am				
	pm				
	pm				
SAT __ / __ / __	am				
	am				
	pm				
	pm				
SUN __ / __ / __	am				
	am				
	pm				
	pm				

Week_____

Weight_____

Mood ☺ ☺ ☺ ☺ ☺

Date	Time	Systolic	Diastolic	Heart Rate	Notes
MON __ /__ /__	am				
	am				
	pm				
	pm				
TUES __ /__ /__	am				
	am				
	pm				
	pm				
WEDS __ /__ /__	am				
	am				
	pm				
	pm				
THURS __ /__ /__	am				
	am				
	pm				
	pm				
FRI __ /__ /__	am				
	am				
	pm				
	pm				
SAT __ /__ /__	am				
	am				
	pm				
	pm				
SUN __ /__ /__	am				
	am				
	pm				
	pm				

Week _____
Weight _____

Mood

Date	Time	Systolic	Diastolic	Heart Rate	Notes
MON __/__/__	am				
	am				
	pm				
	pm				
TUES __/__/__	am				
	am				
	pm				
	pm				
WEDS __/__/__	am				
	am				
	pm				
	pm				
THURS __/__/__	am				
	am				
	pm				
	pm				
FRI __/__/__	am				
	am				
	pm				
	pm				
SAT __/__/__	am				
	am				
	pm				
	pm				
SUN __/__/__	am				
	am				
	pm				
	pm				

Week_____

Weight_____

Mood ☺ ☺ ☺ ☺ ☺

Date	Time	Systolic	Diastolic	Heart Rate	Notes
MON __ / __ / __	am				
	am				
	pm				
	pm				
TUES __ / __ / __	am				
	am				
	pm				
	pm				
WEDS __ / __ / __	am				
	am				
	pm				
	pm				
THURS __ / __ / __	am				
	am				
	pm				
	pm				
FRI __ / __ / __	am				
	am				
	pm				
	pm				
SAT __ / __ / __	am				
	am				
	pm				
	pm				
SUN __ / __ / __	am				
	am				
	pm				
	pm				

Week_____

Weight_____

Mood ☺ ☺ ☺ ☺ ☺

Date	Time	Systolic	Diastolic	Heart Rate	Notes
MON __/__/__	am				
	am				
	pm				
	pm				
TUES __/__/__	am				
	am				
	pm				
	pm				
WEDS __/__/__	am				
	am				
	pm				
	pm				
THURS __/__/__	am				
	am				
	pm				
	pm				
FRI __/__/__	am				
	am				
	pm				
	pm				
SAT __/__/__	am				
	am				
	pm				
	pm				
SUN __/__/__	am				
	am				
	pm				
	pm				

Week _____
Weight _____

Mood ☺ ☺ ☺ ☺ ☺

Date	Time	Systolic	Diastolic	Heart Rate	Notes
MON __/__/__	am				
	am				
	pm				
	pm				
TUES __/__/__	am				
	am				
	pm				
	pm				
WEDS __/__/__	am				
	am				
	pm				
	pm				
THURS __/__/__	am				
	am				
	pm				
	pm				
FRI __/__/__	am				
	am				
	pm				
	pm				
SAT __/__/__	am				
	am				
	pm				
	pm				
SUN __/__/__	am				
	am				
	pm				
	pm				

*Week*_____

*Weight*_____   *Mood* ☺ ☺ ☺ ☺ ☺

Date	Time	Systolic	Diastolic	Heart Rate	Notes
MON __/__/__	am				
	am				
	pm				
	pm				
TUES __/__/__	am				
	am				
	pm				
	pm				
WEDS __/__/__	am				
	am				
	pm				
	pm				
THURS __/__/__	am				
	am				
	pm				
	pm				
FRI __/__/__	am				
	am				
	pm				
	pm				
SAT __/__/__	am				
	am				
	pm				
	pm				
SUN __/__/__	am				
	am				
	pm				
	pm				

Week_____

Weight_____

Mood ☺ ☺ ☺ ☺ ☺

Date	Time	Systolic	Diastolic	Heart Rate	Notes
MON __ / __ / __	am				
	am				
	pm				
	pm				
TUES __ / __ / __	am				
	am				
	pm				
	pm				
WEDS __ / __ / __	am				
	am				
	pm				
	pm				
THURS __ / __ / __	am				
	am				
	pm				
	pm				
FRI __ / __ / __	am				
	am				
	pm				
	pm				
SAT __ / __ / __	am				
	am				
	pm				
	pm				
SUN __ / __ / __	am				
	am				
	pm				
	pm				

*Week*_____

*Weight*_____   *Mood*  ☺ ☺ ☺ ☺ ☺

Date	Time	Systolic	Diastolic	Heart Rate	Notes
MON ___/___/___	am				
	am				
	pm				
	pm				
TUES ___/___/___	am				
	am				
	pm				
	pm				
WEDS ___/___/___	am				
	am				
	pm				
	pm				
THURS ___/___/___	am				
	am				
	pm				
	pm				
FRI ___/___/___	am				
	am				
	pm				
	pm				
SAT ___/___/___	am				
	am				
	pm				
	pm				
SUN ___/___/___	am				
	am				
	pm				
	pm				

*Week*_____

*Weight*_____

Mood ☺ ☺ ☺ ☺ ☺

Date	Time	Systolic	Diastolic	Heart Rate	Notes
MON __/__/__	am				
	am				
	pm				
	pm				
TUES __/__/__	am				
	am				
	pm				
	pm				
WEDS __/__/__	am				
	am				
	pm				
	pm				
THURS __/__/__	am				
	am				
	pm				
	pm				
FRI __/__/__	am				
	am				
	pm				
	pm				
SAT __/__/__	am				
	am				
	pm				
	pm				
SUN __/__/__	am				
	am				
	pm				
	pm				

*Week*_____
*Weight*_____   *Mood*  ☺ ☺ ☺ ☺ ☺

Date	Time	Systolic	Diastolic	Heart Rate	Notes
MON __/__/__	am				
	am				
	pm				
	pm				
TUES __/__/__	am				
	am				
	pm				
	pm				
WEDS __/__/__	am				
	am				
	pm				
	pm				
THURS __/__/__	am				
	am				
	pm				
	pm				
FRI __/__/__	am				
	am				
	pm				
	pm				
SAT __/__/__	am				
	am				
	pm				
	pm				
SUN __/__/__	am				
	am				
	pm				
	pm				

*Week*_____

*Weight*_____

Mood ☺ ☺ ☺ ☺ ☺

Date	Time	Systolic	Diastolic	Heart Rate	Notes
MON __ / __ / __	am				
	am				
	pm				
	pm				
TUES __ / __ / __	am				
	am				
	pm				
	pm				
WEDS __ / __ / __	am				
	am				
	pm				
	pm				
THURS __ / __ / __	am				
	am				
	pm				
	pm				
FRI __ / __ / __	am				
	am				
	pm				
	pm				
SAT __ / __ / __	am				
	am				
	pm				
	pm				
SUN __ / __ / __	am				
	am				
	pm				
	pm				

*Week*_____

*Weight*_____

Mood ☺ ☺ ☺ ☺ ☺

Date	Time	Systolic	Diastolic	Heart Rate	Notes
MON __ / __ / __	am				
	am				
	pm				
	pm				
TUES __ / __ / __	am				
	am				
	pm				
	pm				
WEDS __ / __ / __	am				
	am				
	pm				
	pm				
THURS __ / __ / __	am				
	am				
	pm				
	pm				
FRI __ / __ / __	am				
	am				
	pm				
	pm				
SAT __ / __ / __	am				
	am				
	pm				
	pm				
SUN __ / __ / __	am				
	am				
	pm				
	pm				

*Week*_____

*Weight*_____   *Mood* ☺ ☺ ☺ ☺ ☺

Date	Time	Systolic	Diastolic	Heart Rate	Notes
MON __/__/__	am				
	am				
	pm				
	pm				
TUES __/__/__	am				
	am				
	pm				
	pm				
WEDS __/__/__	am				
	am				
	pm				
	pm				
THURS __/__/__	am				
	am				
	pm				
	pm				
FRI __/__/__	am				
	am				
	pm				
	pm				
SAT __/__/__	am				
	am				
	pm				
	pm				
SUN __/__/__	am				
	am				
	pm				
	pm				

Week_____
Weight_____   Mood ☺ ☺ ☺ ☺ ☺

Date	Time	Systolic	Diastolic	Heart Rate	Notes
MON __/__/__	am				
	am				
	pm				
	pm				
TUES __/__/__	am				
	am				
	pm				
	pm				
WEDS __/__/__	am				
	am				
	pm				
	pm				
THURS __/__/__	am				
	am				
	pm				
	pm				
FRI __/__/__	am				
	am				
	pm				
	pm				
SAT __/__/__	am				
	am				
	pm				
	pm				
SUN __/__/__	am				
	am				
	pm				
	pm				

Week_____

Weight_____

Mood ☺ ☺ ☺ ☺ ☺

Date	Time	Systolic	Diastolic	Heart Rate	Notes
MON __/__/__	am				
	am				
	pm				
	pm				
TUES __/__/__	am				
	am				
	pm				
	pm				
WEDS __/__/__	am				
	am				
	pm				
	pm				
THURS __/__/__	am				
	am				
	pm				
	pm				
FRI __/__/__	am				
	am				
	pm				
	pm				
SAT __/__/__	am				
	am				
	pm				
	pm				
SUN __/__/__	am				
	am				
	pm				
	pm				

Week_____

Weight_____

Mood ☺ ☺ ☺ ☺ ☺

Date	Time	Systolic	Diastolic	Heart Rate	Notes
MON __ / __ / __	am				
	am				
	pm				
	pm				
TUES __ / __ / __	am				
	am				
	pm				
	pm				
WEDS __ / __ / __	am				
	am				
	pm				
	pm				
THURS __ / __ / __	am				
	am				
	pm				
	pm				
FRI __ / __ / __	am				
	am				
	pm				
	pm				
SAT __ / __ / __	am				
	am				
	pm				
	pm				
SUN __ / __ / __	am				
	am				
	pm				
	pm				

Week_____

Weight_____

Mood ☺ ☺ ☺ ☺ ☺

Date	Time	Systolic	Diastolic	Heart Rate	Notes
MON __/__/__	am				
	am				
	pm				
	pm				
TUES __/__/__	am				
	am				
	pm				
	pm				
WEDS __/__/__	am				
	am				
	pm				
	pm				
THURS __/__/__	am				
	am				
	pm				
	pm				
FRI __/__/__	am				
	am				
	pm				
	pm				
SAT __/__/__	am				
	am				
	pm				
	pm				
SUN __/__/__	am				
	am				
	pm				
	pm				

Week_____
Weight_____

Mood  ☺ ☺ ☺ ☺ ☺

Date	Time	Systolic	Diastolic	Heart Rate	Notes
MON __ / __ / __	am				
	am				
	pm				
	pm				
TUES __ / __ / __	am				
	am				
	pm				
	pm				
WEDS __ / __ / __	am				
	am				
	pm				
	pm				
THURS __ / __ / __	am				
	am				
	pm				
	pm				
FRI __ / __ / __	am				
	am				
	pm				
	pm				
SAT __ / __ / __	am				
	am				
	pm				
	pm				
SUN __ / __ / __	am				
	am				
	pm				
	pm				

*Week*_____

*Weight*_____

Mood ☺ ☺ ☺ ☺ ☺

Date	Time	Systolic	Diastolic	Heart Rate	Notes
MON __ / __ / __	am				
	am				
	pm				
	pm				
TUES __ / __ / __	am				
	am				
	pm				
	pm				
WEDS __ / __ / __	am				
	am				
	pm				
	pm				
THURS __ / __ / __	am				
	am				
	pm				
	pm				
FRI __ / __ / __	am				
	am				
	pm				
	pm				
SAT __ / __ / __	am				
	am				
	pm				
	pm				
SUN __ / __ / __	am				
	am				
	pm				
	pm				

Week_____

Weight_____

Mood ☺ ☺ ☺ ☺ ☺

Date	Time	Systolic	Diastolic	Heart Rate	Notes
MON __/__/__	am				
	am				
	pm				
	pm				
TUES __/__/__	am				
	am				
	pm				
	pm				
WEDS __/__/__	am				
	am				
	pm				
	pm				
THURS __/__/__	am				
	am				
	pm				
	pm				
FRI __/__/__	am				
	am				
	pm				
	pm				
SAT __/__/__	am				
	am				
	pm				
	pm				
SUN __/__/__	am				
	am				
	pm				
	pm				

Week _____
Weight _____

Mood ☺ ☺ ☺ ☺ ☺

Date	Time	Systolic	Diastolic	Heart Rate	Notes
MON __/__/__	am				
	am				
	pm				
	pm				
TUES __/__/__	am				
	am				
	pm				
	pm				
WEDS __/__/__	am				
	am				
	pm				
	pm				
THURS __/__/__	am				
	am				
	pm				
	pm				
FRI __/__/__	am				
	am				
	pm				
	pm				
SAT __/__/__	am				
	am				
	pm				
	pm				
SUN __/__/__	am				
	am				
	pm				
	pm				

*Week*_____
*Weight*_____   *Mood* ☺ ☺ ☺ ☺ ☺

Date	Time	Systolic	Diastolic	Heart Rate	Notes
MON __/__/__	am				
	am				
	pm				
	pm				
TUES __/__/__	am				
	am				
	pm				
	pm				
WEDS __/__/__	am				
	am				
	pm				
	pm				
THURS __/__/__	am				
	am				
	pm				
	pm				
FRI __/__/__	am				
	am				
	pm				
	pm				
SAT __/__/__	am				
	am				
	pm				
	pm				
SUN __/__/__	am				
	am				
	pm				
	pm				

Week _____

Weight _____

Mood 😊 😊 😊 😊 😊

Date	Time	Systolic	Diastolic	Heart Rate	Notes
MON __ / __ / __	am				
	am				
	pm				
	pm				
TUES __ / __ / __	am				
	am				
	pm				
	pm				
WEDS __ / __ / __	am				
	am				
	pm				
	pm				
THURS __ / __ / __	am				
	am				
	pm				
	pm				
FRI __ / __ / __	am				
	am				
	pm				
	pm				
SAT __ / __ / __	am				
	am				
	pm				
	pm				
SUN __ / __ / __	am				
	am				
	pm				
	pm				

Week_____

Weight_____

Mood ☺ ☺ ☺ ☺ ☺

Date	Time	Systolic	Diastolic	Heart Rate	Notes
MON __ / __ / __	am				
	am				
	pm				
	pm				
TUES __ / __ / __	am				
	am				
	pm				
	pm				
WEDS __ / __ / __	am				
	am				
	pm				
	pm				
THURS __ / __ / __	am				
	am				
	pm				
	pm				
FRI __ / __ / __	am				
	am				
	pm				
	pm				
SAT __ / __ / __	am				
	am				
	pm				
	pm				
SUN __ / __ / __	am				
	am				
	pm				
	pm				

Week_____
Weight_____

Mood ☺ ☺ ☺ ☺ ☺

Date	Time	Systolic	Diastolic	Heart Rate	Notes
MON __/__/__	am				
	am				
	pm				
	pm				
TUES __/__/__	am				
	am				
	pm				
	pm				
WEDS __/__/__	am				
	am				
	pm				
	pm				
THURS __/__/__	am				
	am				
	pm				
	pm				
FRI __/__/__	am				
	am				
	pm				
	pm				
SAT __/__/__	am				
	am				
	pm				
	pm				
SUN __/__/__	am				
	am				
	pm				
	pm				

*Week*_____

*Weight*_____

Mood ☺ ☺ ☺ ☺ ☺

Date	Time	Systolic	Diastolic	Heart Rate	Notes
MON __ / __ / __	am				
	am				
	pm				
	pm				
TUES __ / __ / __	am				
	am				
	pm				
	pm				
WEDS __ / __ / __	am				
	am				
	pm				
	pm				
THURS __ / __ / __	am				
	am				
	pm				
	pm				
FRI __ / __ / __	am				
	am				
	pm				
	pm				
SAT __ / __ / __	am				
	am				
	pm				
	pm				
SUN __ / __ / __	am				
	am				
	pm				
	pm				

Week _____

Weight _____

Mood ☺ ☺ ☺ ☺ ☺

Date	Time	Systolic	Diastolic	Heart Rate	Notes
MON __ / __ / __	am				
	am				
	pm				
	pm				
TUES __ / __ / __	am				
	am				
	pm				
	pm				
WEDS __ / __ / __	am				
	am				
	pm				
	pm				
THURS __ / __ / __	am				
	am				
	pm				
	pm				
FRI __ / __ / __	am				
	am				
	pm				
	pm				
SAT __ / __ / __	am				
	am				
	pm				
	pm				
SUN __ / __ / __	am				
	am				
	pm				
	pm				

Week_____
Weight_____

Mood ☺ ☺ ☺ ☺ ☺

Date	Time	Systolic	Diastolic	Heart Rate	Notes
MON __ / __ / __	am				
	am				
	pm				
	pm				
TUES __ / __ / __	am				
	am				
	pm				
	pm				
WEDS __ / __ / __	am				
	am				
	pm				
	pm				
THURS __ / __ / __	am				
	am				
	pm				
	pm				
FRI __ / __ / __	am				
	am				
	pm				
	pm				
SAT __ / __ / __	am				
	am				
	pm				
	pm				
SUN __ / __ / __	am				
	am				
	pm				
	pm				

*Week*_____

*Weight*_____   *Mood* ☺ ☺ ☺ ☺ ☺

Date	Time	Systolic	Diastolic	Heart Rate	Notes
MON __ / __ / __	am				
	am				
	pm				
	pm				
TUES __ / __ / __	am				
	am				
	pm				
	pm				
WEDS __ / __ / __	am				
	am				
	pm				
	pm				
THURS __ / __ / __	am				
	am				
	pm				
	pm				
FRI __ / __ / __	am				
	am				
	pm				
	pm				
SAT __ / __ / __	am				
	am				
	pm				
	pm				
SUN __ / __ / __	am				
	am				
	pm				
	pm				

Week_____

Weight_____

Mood ☺ ☺ ☺ ☺ ☺

Date	Time	Systolic	Diastolic	Heart Rate	Notes
MON __/__/__	am				
	am				
	pm				
	pm				
TUES __/__/__	am				
	am				
	pm				
	pm				
WEDS __/__/__	am				
	am				
	pm				
	pm				
THURS __/__/__	am				
	am				
	pm				
	pm				
FRI __/__/__	am				
	am				
	pm				
	pm				
SAT __/__/__	am				
	am				
	pm				
	pm				
SUN __/__/__	am				
	am				
	pm				
	pm				

*Week*_____

*Weight*_____

Mood ☺ ☺ ☺ ☺ ☺

Date	Time	Systolic	Diastolic	Heart Rate	Notes
MON __/__/__	am				
	am				
	pm				
	pm				
TUES __/__/__	am				
	am				
	pm				
	pm				
WEDS __/__/__	am				
	am				
	pm				
	pm				
THURS __/__/__	am				
	am				
	pm				
	pm				
FRI __/__/__	am				
	am				
	pm				
	pm				
SAT __/__/__	am				
	am				
	pm				
	pm				
SUN __/__/__	am				
	am				
	pm				
	pm				

*Week*_____

*Weight*_____   *Mood* ☺ ☺ ☺ ☺ ☺

Date	Time	Systolic	Diastolic	Heart Rate	Notes
MON __ /__/__	am				
	am				
	pm				
	pm				
TUES __ /__/__	am				
	am				
	pm				
	pm				
WEDS __ /__/__	am				
	am				
	pm				
	pm				
THURS __ /__/__	am				
	am				
	pm				
	pm				
FRI __ /__/__	am				
	am				
	pm				
	pm				
SAT __ /__/__	am				
	am				
	pm				
	pm				
SUN __ /__/__	am				
	am				
	pm				
	pm				

*Week*_____

*Weight*_____

Mood ☺ ☺ ☺ ☺ ☺

Date	Time	Systolic	Diastolic	Heart Rate	Notes
MON __ / __ / __	am				
	am				
	pm				
	pm				
TUES __ / __ / __	am				
	am				
	pm				
	pm				
WEDS __ / __ / __	am				
	am				
	pm				
	pm				
THURS __ / __ / __	am				
	am				
	pm				
	pm				
FRI __ / __ / __	am				
	am				
	pm				
	pm				
SAT __ / __ / __	am				
	am				
	pm				
	pm				
SUN __ / __ / __	am				
	am				
	pm				
	pm				

Week_____

Weight_____

Mood ☺ ☺ ☺ ☺ ☺

Date	Time	Systolic	Diastolic	Heart Rate	Notes
MON __/__/__	am				
	am				
	pm				
	pm				
TUES __/__/__	am				
	am				
	pm				
	pm				
WEDS __/__/__	am				
	am				
	pm				
	pm				
THURS __/__/__	am				
	am				
	pm				
	pm				
FRI __/__/__	am				
	am				
	pm				
	pm				
SAT __/__/__	am				
	am				
	pm				
	pm				
SUN __/__/__	am				
	am				
	pm				
	pm				

Week _____

Weight _____

Mood ☺ ☺ ☺ ☺ ☺

Date	Time	Systolic	Diastolic	Heart Rate	Notes
MON __ / __ / __	am				
	am				
	pm				
	pm				
TUES __ / __ / __	am				
	am				
	pm				
	pm				
WEDS __ / __ / __	am				
	am				
	pm				
	pm				
THURS __ / __ / __	am				
	am				
	pm				
	pm				
FRI __ / __ / __	am				
	am				
	pm				
	pm				
SAT __ / __ / __	am				
	am				
	pm				
	pm				
SUN __ / __ / __	am				
	am				
	pm				
	pm				

Week_____
Weight_____

Mood ☺ ☺ ☺ ☺ ☺

Date	Time	Systolic	Diastolic	Heart Rate	Notes
MON __/__/__	am				
	am				
	pm				
	pm				
TUES __/__/__	am				
	am				
	pm				
	pm				
WEDS __/__/__	am				
	am				
	pm				
	pm				
THURS __/__/__	am				
	am				
	pm				
	pm				
FRI __/__/__	am				
	am				
	pm				
	pm				
SAT __/__/__	am				
	am				
	pm				
	pm				
SUN __/__/__	am				
	am				
	pm				
	pm				

Week_____

Weight_____

Mood ☺ ☺ ☺ ☺ ☺

Date	Time	Systolic	Diastolic	Heart Rate	Notes
MON __ / __ / __	am				
	am				
	pm				
	pm				
TUES __ / __ / __	am				
	am				
	pm				
	pm				
WEDS __ / __ / __	am				
	am				
	pm				
	pm				
THURS __ / __ / __	am				
	am				
	pm				
	pm				
FRI __ / __ / __	am				
	am				
	pm				
	pm				
SAT __ / __ / __	am				
	am				
	pm				
	pm				
SUN __ / __ / __	am				
	am				
	pm				
	pm				

Made in the USA
Monee, IL
24 March 2023

30433774R10059